Michael Rosen's
ScRaPBooK

Michael Rosen

OXFORD
UNIVERSITY PRESS

OXFORD
UNIVERSITY PRESS

Great Clarendon Street, Oxford OX2 6DP

Oxford University Press is a department of the University of Oxford.
It furthers the University's objective of excellence in research, scholarship,
and education by publishing worldwide in

Oxford   New York

Auckland   Cape Town   Dar es Salaam   Hong Kong   Karachi
Kuala Lumpur   Madrid   Melbourne   Mexico City   Nairobi
New Delhi   Shanghai   Taipei   Toronto

With offices in

Argentina   Austria   Brazil   Chile   Czech Republic   France   Greece
Guatemala   Hungary   Italy   Japan   Poland   Portugal   Singapore
South Korea   Switzerland   Thailand   Turkey   Ukraine   Vietnam

Oxford is a registered trade mark of Oxford University Press
in the UK and in certain other countries

British Library Cataloguing in Publication Data

Data available

ISBN-13: 978-0-19-917941-1
ISBN-10: 0-19-917941-7

3 5 7 9 10 8 6 4 2

Printed in China by Imago

Acknowledgements

The publisher would like to thank the following for permission to reproduce
photographs: Rob Judges/OUP **p3**, **p7**, **p8**, **p13**, **p15**b, **p17**, **p23**, **p26**, **p28**b, **p29**b, **p31**, **p32**

All other photographs kindly supplied by Michael Rosen

Illustrations by: **p4** Andy Hamilton, **p9**, **p11** Bill Greenhead/Illustration Limited,
p22 Martin Aston, **p25**, **p31** Jan Lewis

Illustrations on **p6**, **p12**, **p18**, **p19**, **p20**, **p21** from QB Archive by kind permission of
A P Wyatt Limited on behalf of Quentin Blake

Cover photograph by Rob Judges/OUP

Every effort has been made to contact copyright holders of material
reproduced in this book. If notified, the publishers will be pleased to
rectify any errors or omissions at the earliest opportunity

Hi. I'm Michael Rosen. Most of the poems I write are to do with my experiences and observations in my life. Read some of my poems and my comments on what they are about.

Contents

This is something that really happened. My brother, Brian, and I mostly got on well together but sometimes we had fights. When this happened, the big question was: who started it? Because I was the younger brother, I was sure that I was the one most hard done by. I was sure that my older brother was to blame. I thought that the whole thing could be solved by asking my mother the key question: who started the very first fight? It would have to be my brother, wouldn't it?

Who Started It?

When me and my brother have a fight
my mum says:
'Stoppit – someone'll get hurt.'

And we say:
'He started it.'
'I didn't. He started it.'

I say:
'Mum, who started the very first fight
between me and Brian?'

And she says:
'You.'

'Me? But I'm four years younger than him.
How could it have been me?'

You see how indignant I'm being? I'm so sure that it can't be me. When you read poems that have conversations in them, it's good fun to try and 'do' the voices, just as if you were reading lines from a play. So this bit of speech that I'm saying here should be said in one of those squeaky, 'it's-not-fair' kind of voices.

And she says.
'Well, it was like this …

You were about two years old
and Brian was six.
You were sitting in your high chair
eating your breakfast
and Brian walked past.
You leaned forward
and banged him over the head
with your spoon.'

'There you are,' says my brother,
'you started it,
you started it.
I always knew you started it.'

My brother wasn't usually quite as triumphant as this, but he did like to be proved right. (Don't we all?!) He liked to have evidence, a bit like a lawyer, to prove something once and for all. And here was my mother giving him just that. Of course, even now, I don't believe this is really what happened. Surely he started the first fight, didn't he?

MRS TOWNSEND

Every time I see Mrs Townsend
she says
O I remember you, you rascal
I can see it now
Your mum and dad was out
looking for you
you was only three
you had gone missing.

You know where they found you?
Halfway up the road
outside the methodist church
running along in your little vest
you didn't have nothing else on
you had left home
with just your vest on
everything else open to the weather
can you imagine?

Well you would never think of that
to look at you now,
would you?

NO

Mrs Townsend featured quite a lot in my life. She, her husband and their son, Keith, lived a few yards from us. We lived in flats over the top of the shops — we were over an estate agent's called 'Norman and Butt' and the Townsends lived over the butchers'. Mr Townsend was the butcher and quite often Mrs Townsend looked after me while Keith and I played out in the alleyway behind the shops and over the park.

This is exactly how she told it to me. This church was about two hundred metres from our flat and seemed to me to look more like a modern school than a church. (Mostly, I only ever went inside very old churches because my parents liked to look at them when we were on holiday.)

If you're reading this out loud, you have to shout this 'NO' quite loudly and rather angrily. For many years, I didn't like to be reminded of this story. Just thinking about it made me feel rather vulnerable as if I was still in some sort of danger.

Again this is a true story and one that I'm not particularly proud of. In this poem I've not only tried to show you what people were saying, but also what I was thinking. Instead of saying, 'I was thinking...' or something like that, I've simply put the words of my thoughts into italics.

Do you ever have the sense of something getting worse, but there's nothing you can do about it? This is what's happening here. Just in case you don't know, 'Woollies' is 'Woolworth's', the big store where my friends and I used to like to go. It was on the corner of the main street on the way to the park.

Now it's getting really bad, and I think Harrybo is trying to cover up for me. He was my very, very, very best friend and we did everything together. He doesn't want me to get into trouble with my dad.

STEALING

Harrybo says:
'That's the best toy car you've nicked yet, it's –'

My dad walks in behind him.
'What did you just say, Harrybo?'

Great! He didn't hear Harrybo properly.

Harrybo turns round –
'... about the car – the – er ...'
'What car?'

Oh no! The questioning.

'Whose car is it?'
Together we say:
'It's Harrybo's.' 'It's Michael's.'
'Where's it from?'
'Woollies.'
'So who paid for it?'
Together we say:
'Him.' 'Him.'
'It couldn't have been you, Michael, you haven't got any money.
Where did you get the money from, Harrybo?'
'I didn't have the – er actually ...'

It's all just about to blow up.

continued

'Look, tell me if I got this wrong:
did I or did I not hear Harrybo say:
"It's the best toy car you've nicked yet"?'

There's no escape.

'Yiss.'
'What do you think Harrybo meant
when he said that?'

Play dumb.

'I'm not really sure.'
'Harrybo, what did you mean
when you said:
"It's the best toy car you've nicked yet"?'
Silence.
'Do you think Michael nicked the car?'
'Oh no. I wouldn't think he'd do a thing like that.'

Fool, Harrybo. He'll pounce on that.

'See, Michael, even your best friend …'

My best friend!

'… thinks you're not the sort of person
who'd do a thing like that.
Aren't you really sick of yourself?'

*Course Harrybo doesn't think that.
He's got a Bluebird racing car
that he nicked as well
in his trouser pocket.*

You have to imagine my dad talking carefully and strongly here — perhaps pointing in time to the words and making each word sound out. He was a teacher and perhaps he learnt how to talk like that when he was in a big classroom full of loud teenagers!

Here's Harrybo trying his best again, sticking up for me. He's trying to do that thing that people sometimes have to do in court: 'vouch for someone's character'. The only trouble here is that my dad isn't fooled. It's only going to make things worse!

'Yiss.'
'Well, you know what you're going to do, don't you?'
'Yiss.'
'What?'
'Take it back.'
'Exactly. And when you get back here you, me and your mother are going to have a long talk about this, aren't we?'

I thought we just had.

'Aren't we?'
'Yiss.'

Oh no, 'the talk'. That's when things are really bad. It's much worse than getting yelled at. You know: the long slow talk where people go over all the things you've done wrong. Not much fun, eh?

This is my dear dad. I think he's forgotten about the toy car.

BOY FRIENDS

Christine Elkins said to me
under the oak tree
in the Memorial Park –
'I've got $2\frac{1}{2}$ boyfriends.'
'$2\frac{1}{2}$?' I said. '$2\frac{1}{2}$?'
'How do you work that out?'

'You, Harrybo, Timmy and Rodge,'
she said.
I thought for a moment …
'Me, Harrybo, Timmy and Rodge?
… 4!'
I was just about to say,
'But that makes 4 –'
when suddenly I thought,
'She has halves – HALF boyfriends! …
… 2 halves make one? No. 3 halves plus 1 … yes
But, which ones are the halves?' I thought …
'and who's The One –
THE One?'

I never dared ask her
so I never found out.

- Yet another true story. The picture you can see is of the very same oak tree, fifty years after Christine and I had this conversation. By the way, how good are you at sums? Especially, those sums where you have to work out wholes and halves? You'll need to be quite good at them to figure this poem out!

$$4 = 2\tfrac{1}{2} \, ?$$

$$* + * + * + 1$$

$$\downarrow$$

$$\tfrac{1}{2} + \tfrac{1}{2} + \tfrac{1}{2} + 1$$

This is my slow brain trying to work out what Christine meant. Do you get it? There were four boys she said were her boyfriends, but it only came to two and a half. So I had to work out how you can divide up four so that it made two and a half. It was only when I figured out that three of us were halves and only one of us was a whole 'One' that I stumbled on the truth.

Harrybo

People often say to me
'What's become of Harrybo,
the boy in your poems?'

And I say:
'When I was 11
we had to do an exam
called the 11-plus.
I passed and went to a Grammar School.
Harrybo failed
and went to a Secondary Modern School.

So though up till then
we used to see each other every day
- weekends as well -
after that,
we didn't see much of each other at all.
I'd see him from the bus
talking with his new friends
and I was with mine.
One time when we met
he told me that once
him and his girlfriend were snogging
in his front room
and his mum was looking in
through the window.
It sounded very different from exploring
the ponds
and making go-karts.

Michael

Harrybo

continued

You may not know that I've often written about Harrybo, not just in the one about stealing. My favourite is the one about the go-kart that you can find in *Quick, Let's Get Out of Here*. Between the ages of seven and eleven, we were best friends. It was just one of those friendships that really clicked. He was very funny, he knew lots of rude rhymes and he seemed to know so much about machines, apples, animals, woods, and places I had never heard of, like Gillingham and Brixham. He lived with his mum, dad and granny about four hundred metres from my flat.

It makes me quite sad to read this. Just going to different schools put something between us. I got together with a couple of boys at my new school and he got in with a big crowd at his new school. My school was called Harrow Weald County Grammar School. His was called Headstone Lane Secondary Modern School.

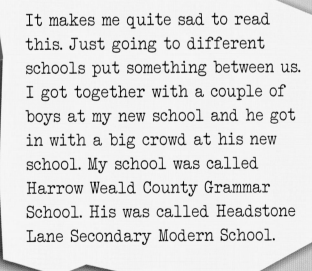

Harrybo's house

When I was 17
we moved
and I didn't see him again.

When I was 38
I visited my old school
and a boy said his dad knew me
from when we were children
and he would like me to come back
for tea at his place.

When I got there
I found out it was Jimmy.
Giggly Jimmy, who hopped about on one foot
if he thought something was funny.
He's a truck driver now.
Jimmy said:
'Harrybo died when he was 17.
I don't know where his parents are.
They moved.'

Before Jimmy told me this
I had sometimes wondered
if somewhere some time
Harrybo had read all these things
I've been writing about him …
But he hadn't.

Sometimes, someone will say something that stuns you. It comes straight out of the blue and changes everything you thought, up until that moment. This is one of those moments for me. I had run the picture in my mind over and over again, that I would one day meet Harrybo, and now I realised that I never would. His real name, by the way, was Brian Harrison.

There ought to be a word for this feeling: imagining that someone is reacting to something you've done but they're not. You know the kind of thing: when you do something, saying to yourself: 'This'll show her!' but in fact that person didn't know anything about it. It feels like shouting in an empty cave.

Eddie in Bed

Sometimes I look really tired,
because you see
when most people are fast asleep
and I'm fast asleep
I hear,
'waaaaaaaaaaaaaaaaaaaaaaaaaaaaaaaa.'
That's the baby, Eddie.
So I get out of bed and go into his room
and he's sitting up in bed
and he has these nightmares.
Not nightmares like you have,
like Dracula biting your head off or something.
He has nightmares about people taking food
away from him.
So one night I go in there
and he's sitting up in bed
lifting his arms above his head
and banging them down
screaming,
'I want my biscuits I want my biscuits.'

Yes, you have to do quite a lot of imagining here. Joe and Eddie are my first two children and Susanna is their mother. In this story, Eddie is about two and Joe is about six. By the way, it's a great story to act out; one group of you could read the words and four others could do the actions.

Now if you can imagine that,
you can also imagine
that at this time he was sleeping
in the same bed as his brother.
Who was six.
And you have to imagine his brother's head
is right next to Eddie's hip.
Think about it.
Eddie's hands go above his head and
Wham
down by his side
right down on Joe's nut.
'I want my biscuits I want my biscuits.'
So Joe lifts his head and goes,
'What's going on?'
Wham
'I want my biscuits.'
'What's going on?'
Wham
'I want my biscuits.'
'What's going on?'
Wham
'I want my biscuits.'

If you're an older child in a family and with an age gap as big as four years, then you'll know just how Joe was feeling here. You used to have a peaceful fun life and then this terrible baby turns up smashing up your toys, making a gigantic noise and waking you up in the night. It shouldn't be allowed!

continued

19

Hmmm. Over the years, I've often had to say this to myself. If you want to see the most stupid thing of all, then you'll find it in *You Wait Till I'm Older Than You* — the story of how Eddie aged three, drove the car into a ditch in France!

'Stop it, Eddie' — wham back
'I want my biscuits.'
Wham.
'Ok, fellas,' I say,
'Cut it out.'
And I lift Eddie up and I take him into our bed.

What a stupid thing to do.

You see
Most people sleep with their head
on the pillow
and their feet at the other end of the bed.
When Eddie comes into our bed
he sleeps with his head next to Susanna's head
and his feet in my ear.

And you have to imagine those feet
sticking in my ear.
And the toes.
Those toes are going
wiggle wiggly wiggly
Down my ear.
All night.
So by the time I get up
in the morning
I'm very tired
and very cross.

Can this really be true? Are mums or dads ever tired and cross? Surely this isn't possible! Oh well, at least I'm admitting it here. Do you notice how I break the lines up? On one line there's 'I'm very tired', and on the other 'and very cross'. I hope that makes you slow down and read one line, pause a moment, and then read the other.

But I can always get my own back on him
in the morning
cos he hates having his nappy done ...

And if you want to find out what a crazy fandango THAT was, then you can find that in *Quick, Let's Get Out of Here*. There you'll find out just what I did with that very, very, very cold cream!

For Naomi

I'm the kind of dad
my children don't want to be seen with
because I'm the kind of dad who

shouts in shops
says hello to babies
doesn't clean the car
eats pizzas in the street
doesn't cut his moustache
sings on buses
argues with policemen
waves to old ladies
has long hair
and
writes poems

Naomi is one of my step-daughters. I helped bring her up for about eleven years starting when she was about seven. Looking back on this poem I think it's about me trying to figure out what kind of dad I was to her.

Oh dear, what a list of embarrassing things! I just wish that my children had brought me up better.

Again, can you see that I've put each item in the list on a new line, just as you would if you were making a shopping list. I hope that stops you from running each item straight into the other and gives you time to think about each thing.

Obviously the last one on the list is the very, very, very worst. Just how embarrassing can a dad get?

As you can see, this is a poem made up of the things people have said to me, the things I've said and thought and the things my daughter has said to me. I wrote it because I was thinking about how I repeat what my parents and teachers said to me even though, at the time, I didn't really know what they meant.

What my mother meant by 'bagels in my socks' is that my socks looked as if my legs had gone through the hole in a bagel and the ring of the bagel made the wrinkle.

'There is a green hill far away' was a hymn that we sang at school. They explained that 'without' in the song meant 'outside'.

They Said, I Say

Whenever my mother left the house,
she'd say: 'Where's my hat? I'm going.'
I didn't understand.
'But you haven't got a hat,' I'd say.

Whenever I had wrinkles in my socks,
my mother would say:
'Take the bagels out of your socks.'
I didn't understand.
I'd say, 'I haven't got any bagels in my socks.'

When I went to school,
we sang:
'There is a green hill far away
without a city wall.'
I didn't understand.
I'd say, 'Green hills don't have city walls.'

At secondary school,
whenever our history teacher lost her temper,
she'd say: 'Great Scott! You're for the high jump.'
I didn't understand.
Who was Scott? Why was he great?
And why did we have to do a high jump?

The teacher who said, 'Great Scott, etc' was Miss Drury. She was about sixty or so in 1957, so she was born before 1900! Who do you think Scott was?

As you'll see when you get to the part of this book called 'Writing Poems', I was having some thoughts about walking to nursery with my daughter. They've popped up in this poem. Writing poems can sometimes be like collecting bits and pieces of a jig-saw and trying to see how they fit together.

As we leave for nursery school in the morning,
I say to my four-year-old daughter:
'Where's my hat? I'm going.'
And she says, 'But you haven't got a hat.'

I look at her socks and say:
'Take the bagels out of your socks.'
And she says, 'I haven't got bagels
in my socks.'

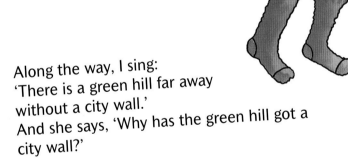

Along the way, I sing:
'There is a green hill far away
without a city wall.'
And she says, 'Why has the green hill got a
city wall?'

And when I say goodbye to her,
I say: 'Great Scott! You're for the high jump.'
And she says,
'No I'm not.'

The Story of Me

I was born in Harrow in north London and we lived in the part of Harrow called Pinner, in a flat just off the main street at 6A Love Lane. (That road name nearly always caused a giggle if I ever had to read it out in class!) My mother used to tell me that I was born the night that the church next door burnt down. Our flat was over an estate agent's called 'Norman and Butt'. They had those names, my father said, because Norman would say 'Hey, how about we start buying up houses near the park?' Then Butt would interrupt: 'Bu-u-u-ut'.

When my dad told me stories like this, I almost believed him. Then I would realize they were just that: stories! When we went to the zoo and saw the sign 'These animals are dangerous', he made the word 'dangerous' rhyme with 'kangaroos'. So he said, 'Ah, it says here that these animals are dangaroos. I've never heard of them before...'

My brother is four years older than me and we shared a bedroom on the top floor of the flat. He was like a third parent to me. I remember him making me recite the long word lists at the back of a reading book and us falling about laughing because the last word on the list was the word 'end'.

He could imitate our mum and dad telling us off so that when it came to one of us really getting told off, we would look at each other and giggle because our parents would end up saying the very same things.

Meanwhile, my mother used to read to me every night and it got me on to reading by myself. My favourites were either books about the past or books about animals.

When I was seven, I made friends with Brian Harrison, who we called Harrybo. He became my closest friend and we spent hours and hours together. In our last year in primary school, we had a teacher who was very, very strict, and I don't think she liked boys very much. She never called us by our first names, though she always called the girls by their first names – oh yes – and her three favourite boys too! Our little gang spent a lot of time giggling behind her back and making up jokes.

Michael

Harrybo

Back at my old school, nearly fifty years after I left it.

All this life was quite separate from two other lives I lived. One was with my grandparents, and the other was holidays. My mother's parents lived on the other side of London in what seemed like a very old, run-down little flat with an outside toilet and chickens in the garden. My parents are Jewish and we would eat Jewish food and use words from a language called Yiddish. So I called my grandmother 'Bubbe' and my grandfather 'Zeyde'.

The other life was when we went camping and walking. We explored Wales, Northumberland, the New Forest, the Yorkshire Moors, Devon and places in France and Germany. I got to love climbing hills, bird watching, helping farmers get in the sheep and cows and walking about with them all day all over their fields.

After Secondary School, I went first to Medical School – I thought I wanted to be a doctor, but I changed my mind and studied English at Oxford University. After that, I worked for a while at the BBC and went to a film school, but since 1976, I've done a mixture of things: writing, teaching, doing my one-man show, appearing on radio and TV and being a husband and father.

Writing Poems

One of the great things about poetry is that there is no *one* single way to write a poem. You can make it rhyme, or you can decide it doesn't have to rhyme. It can be a conversation, or a single person speaking. It can be a stream of thoughts, or it can be a mixture of thoughts and the things people say. If you want to, you can just describe something that you can see; if you prefer, you can describe something you've imagined. Or again, you can just make it tell a story.

So, how do you write a poem? Try reading a lot of poems. Let yourself be amazed that people can write in so many different ways. Watch what people do, listen to what people say. Write down anything that strikes you as interesting, mysterious, odd or funny. The same goes for the poems you read; if anything catches your attention, scribble it down in a notebook.

Try playing around with words – write things that sound impossible:

'a furious hat',

'I ran into the bottle',

'even the lemon needs friends'.

It's evening as I'm writing the words that you're reading now. This morning I was walking to school with my four-year-old daughter. It was raining, she was wearing a bright yellow mac and her yellow 'duck boots' (amazingly, they really do look like ducks). She was splashing in the puddles. I wondered about writing a poem about the walk between our house and her nursery school. I started to make a little list in my notebook of the things we see together and talk about.

A lot of writing is like that. It'll crop up. It may surprise you. If it surprises you, it may well surprise other people and people like to be surprised by what they read.

A World of Poetry

Here are the names of some modern poets whose poems you may like reading: Valerie Bloom, Roger McGough, Matthew Sweeney, John Agard, Kit Wright, Jackie Kay, Carol Ann Duffy, Brian Patten, Ted Hughes, Lindsay MacRae.

Some poets from a while ago you might like are: Walter de la Mare, A A Milne, Eleanor Farjeon and Rudyard Kipling. Further ago: Robert Louis Stevenson, Edward Lear, Lewis Carroll. And even further back: John Keats, Samuel Taylor Coleridge and William Shakespeare.

Some American poets you might like are: Eve Merriam, Langston Hughes, Jack Prelutsky, Shel Silverstein and Carl Sandburg.

By the way, enjoy your writing!

Michael Rosen

Some of my books...

Fiction and Picture books
Hairy Tales and Nursery Crimes
You're Thinking About Doughnuts
Clever Cakes
Burping Bertha
This Is Our House
Snore!
Mission Ziffoid
Rover
Lovely Old Roly
Oww!
Howler
Michael Rosen's Sad Book
You're Thinking About Tomatoes
We're Going On A Bear Hunt
Little Rabbit Foo Foo
Zoo At Night
You Wait Till I'm Older Than You
Tea In The Sugar Bowl, Potato
    In My Shoe

The Michael Rosen Book of
    Nonsense
Lunch Boxes Don't Fly
Centrally Heated Knickers
Even More Nonsense
Uncle Billy Being Silly
No Breathing In Class
Alphabet Poem
Smelly Jelly Smelly Fish
Under The Bed
Hard-Boiled Legs
Spollyollydiddlytiddlyitis
Silly Stories
The Wicked tricks of Till
    Owlyglass
The Golem of Old Prague
The Man With No Shadow
William Shakespeare's
    Romeo and Juliet

Anthologies
The Kingfisher Book of
    Children's Poetry
A Spider Bought A Bicycle
The Kingfisher Book of Funny
    Stories
A World of Poetry
Sonsense Nongs
Poems for the Very Young
A Different Story; Poems from
    the Past
Walking the Bridge of Your Nose
Classic Poetry – An Illustrated
    Collection
Night-Night, Knight, And
    Other Poems

For more books, see my website:

http://www.michaelrosen.co.uk